VERBAL REASONING 2

PAPERS 5 – 8
(Multiple choice format)

Mary and Barbara Walsh M.A. (Oxon), P.G.C.E.

For Oliver, Rebecca, Harry and Sophie

ISBN   (10 digit)   0-9553099-1-3
ISBN   (13 digit)   978-0-9553099-1-5

Published by bumblebee (UK) Limited
Registered Office: 4 The Sanctuary, 23 Oakhill Grove, Surbiton, Surrey KT6 6DU

Paper 5

In the following questions, find **one** word from the top row and **one** word from the bottom row that will join together to form **one** correctly spelt new word.
The order of the letters does not change.

The word from the top row always comes first.

Mark **both** words on the answer sheet.

Example

       (he   she   we)
       (am   at   are)

Answer

      he   **at**   (the word is **heat**)

QUESTION **1**

(pat   cot   ever)
(one   age   ton)

QUESTION **2**

(tap   use   peas)
(sing   full   ant)

QUESTION **3**

(car   he   are)
(pit   rear   art)

QUESTION **4**

(car   plum   at)
(our   am   age)

QUESTION **5**

(pup   can   ape)
(pit   ear   did)

QUESTION **6**

(miss   disc   tape)
(cord   lame   over)

QUESTION **7**

(plain   neck   at)
(tack   lass   tick)

In the following questions, take a letter from the first word and move it into the second word to form two new words.

All the other letters must stay in the same order and both new words must make sense.

Work out which letter moves and mark it on the answer sheet.

Example

      heart   camp

Answer

      r   (the two new words are **heat** and **cramp**)

QUESTION **8**

stand   peal

QUESTION **9**

regal   raged

QUESTION **10**

quiet   quip

QUESTION **11**

table   lazed

QUESTION **12**

below   cap

QUESTION **13**

snore   meat

QUESTION **14**

fiend   card

KEEP GOING

GO STRAIGHT ON

In these questions, letters represent numbers. Work out the answer to each sum, find its letter and mark it on the answer sheet.

Example

If A=4,   B=3,   C=2,   D=6,   E=1,

what is the answer to this sum **as a letter**?

$$(B \times A) \div C = [\ ?\ ]$$

Answer

D

QUESTION **15**

If A=10,   B=4,   C=7,   D=3,   E=24,

what is the answer to this sum **as a letter**?

$$E - D - C - B = [\ ?\ ]$$

QUESTION **16**

If A=6,   B=2,   C=4,   D=3,   E=12,

what is the answer to this sum **as a letter**?

$$A \times A \times B \div E = [\ ?\ ]$$

QUESTION **17**

If A=3,   B=7,   C=1,   D=0,   E=5,

what is the answer to this sum **as a letter**?

$$A + E - B = [\ ?\ ]$$

QUESTION **18**

If A=2,   B=3,   C=4,   D=9,   E=6,

what is the answer to this sum **as a letter**?

$$(A \times D) \div E = [\ ?\ ]$$

KEEP GOING

QUESTION **19**

If A=24,   B=9,   C=12,   D=3,   E=5,

what is the answer to this sum **as a letter**?

$$A - (D \times E) = [\ ?\ ]$$

QUESTION **20**

If A=8,   B=3,   C=5,   D=6,   E=13,

what is the answer to this sum **as a letter**?

$$2A - B - C = [\ ?\ ]$$

QUESTION **21**

If A=12,   B=4,   C=9,   D=17,   E=5,

what is the answer to this sum **as a letter**?

$$A + C - D = [\ ?\ ]$$

Read the following information, then work out the correct answer to the question and mark it on the answer sheet.

QUESTION **22**

Natalie and Anita play netball.
Alyssa and Natalie play hockey.
Anita and Alyssa play rounders.

Which of the following statements is true?

a. Alyssa only plays hockey.

b. Natalie plays netball and rounders.

c. Alyssa plays all three games.

d. Anita plays soccer.

e. Natalie plays netball and hockey.

GO STRAIGHT ON

In each sentence there is a word of **four** letters hidden between the end of one word and the beginning of the next.

Find the pair of words that contains the hidden word and mark your answer on the answer sheet.

Example

He skis so badly.

Answer

skis so (the hidden word is **kiss**)

QUESTION **23**

The car engine made strange noises.

QUESTION **24**

My dog really enjoys his food!

QUESTION **25**

We admit children accompanied by adults.

QUESTION **26**

Why do men love computer games?

QUESTION **27**

Go left at the next roundabout.

QUESTION **28**

Who made these delicious jam tarts?

QUESTION **29**

The games start punctually at eight.

QUESTION **30**

You are not allowed to swear.

KEEP GOING

In the following questions, three of the five words are related in some way.

Find the **two** words that do **not** go with these three and mark them **both** on the answer sheet.

Example

carrot   turnip   mango   pea   apple

Answer

mango   apple

QUESTION **31**

vacant plain simple empty unadorned

QUESTION **32**

barley oats mint parsley wheat

QUESTION **33**

hazard sanctuary peril danger safety

QUESTION **34**

herring cod lobster sole crab

QUESTION **35**

elm poplar friendly birch sociable

QUESTION **36**

hoax trick entice persuade coax

QUESTION **37**

granite platinum silver marble gold

GO STRAIGHT ON

Find **two** words, **one** from the top row and **one** from the bottom row, that are **closest in meaning**.

Mark **both** words on the answer sheet.

Example

(scent   glass   fragrant)
(bottle   liquid   odour)

Answer

scent   odour

QUESTION **38**

(rehearsed   play   theatre)
(acted   practised   danced)

QUESTION **39**

(tough   valiant   vigorous)
(tender   lean   courageous)

QUESTION **40**

(orange   pip   core)
(heart   apple   peel)

QUESTION **41**

(quiet   din   study)
(exam   pass   noise)

QUESTION **42**

(follow   enter   consequence)
(lead   outcome   exit)

QUESTION **43**

(height   top   aptitude)
(bottom   width   altitude)

QUESTION **44**

(recount   family   square)
(number   figure   relate)

QUESTION **45**

(strike   shy   hit)
(coconut   stable   bashful)

KEEP GOING

In the following questions, find the number that will complete the sum correctly and mark it on the answer sheet.

Example

$$8 \times 3 \div 2 = 5 \times 3 - [\ ?\ ]$$

Answer

3

QUESTION **46**

$$(46 + 26) \div 6 = 2 \times 4 + [\ ?\ ]$$

QUESTION **47**

$$6 \times 5 + 6 = 2 \times 15 + [\ ?\ ]$$

QUESTION **48**

$$121 \div 11 + 9 = 3 \times 6 + [\ ?\ ]$$

QUESTION **49**

$$26 - 12 + 6 = 10 + 19 - [\ ?\ ]$$

QUESTION **50**

$$9 \times 5 - 5 = 22 - 12 + [\ ?\ ]$$

QUESTION **51**

$$49 \div 7 + 4 = 16 \div 2 + [\ ?\ ]$$

QUESTION **52**

$$4 \times 7 - 15 = 9 \times 3 - [\ ?\ ]$$

GO STRAIGHT ON

Read the following information, then work out the correct answer to the question and mark it on the answer sheet.

QUESTION **53**

Three trains travel from Bramble Edge to Pendle every morning.

Train 1 leaves Bramble Edge at 11.15am.
Train 2 leaves Bramble Edge at 11am and is twice as fast as Train 3.
Train 3 leaves 30 minutes after Train 1 and arrives in Pendle at 12.15.

What time does Train 2 arrive in Pendle?

a. 11.00 am

b. 11.15 am

c. 11.30 am

d. 11.45 am

e. 12 noon

KEEP GOING

In each of the following sentences, **three letters next to each other** have been removed from the word in capitals. These three letters make one correctly spelt word without changing their order. Find the missing three letter word and mark it on the answer sheet. The sentence must make sense.

Example

The cock **CED** loudly every morning.

Answer

ROW (The word in capitals is **CROWED**)

QUESTION **54**

The boy spent **HS** on his project.

QUESTION **55**

Nowadays, few men wear **BER** hats.

QUESTION **56**

The headmaster will not **TOLTE** bad behaviour.

QUESTION **57**

The police **SCHED** the lady's handbag.

QUESTION **58**

The prize for the **COMITION** is £100.

QUESTION **59**

You need a **SDY** hand to be a surgeon.

QUESTION **60**

Rivers often have several **TRIARIES**.

GO STRAIGHT ON

Each question below contains three pairs of words. Find the word that completes the last pair of words in the **same way** as the other two pairs. Mark your answer on the answer sheet.

Example

(three   the)   (shame   she)
(bacon   [?])

Answer   **ban**

QUESTION **61**

(flower   low)   (stopper   top)
(branch   [?])

QUESTION **62**

(peculiar   pear)   (favourite   fate)
(sensational   [?])

QUESTION **63**

(tern   stern)   (bout   about)
(pen   [?])

QUESTION **64**

(make   male)   (pert   pest)
(mass   [?])

QUESTION **65**

(matter   team)   (pepper   peep)
(dampen   [?])

QUESTION **66**

(cue   cube)   (cale   cable)
(fire   [?])

QUESTION **67**

(lantern   near)   (beakers   seer)
(ballets   [?])

KEEP GOING

ABCDEFGHIJKLMNOPQRSTUVWXYZ

The alphabet is here to help you with the following questions.

Work out which pair of letters will come next in the series and mark your answer on the answer sheet.

Example

LX   MW   NV   OU   [?]

Answer

PT

QUESTION **68**

TU   SW   RY   QA   PC   [?]

QUESTION **69**

MY   OW   RT   TR   WO   [?]

QUESTION **70**

JZ   KY   MW   PT   TP   [?]

QUESTION **71**

ZC   XF   VI   TL   RO   [?]

QUESTION **72**

TU   XY   BC   FG   JK   [?]

QUESTION **73**

KY   QV   VS   ZP   CM   [?]

QUESTION **74**

CZ   EX   HU   LQ   QL   [?]

GO STRAIGHT ON

Three of these four words are written in number code.

The codes are **not** written in the same order as the words and one of the codes is missing.

MEET   MOON   MOAN   MEAN

3265   3114   3225

Work out the correct code for each word and answer the following questions.

Mark the correct answer on the answer sheet.

QUESTION **75**

Which word has the number code **3165**?

QUESTION **76**

What is the code for the word **TAME**?

QUESTION **77**

What is the code for the word **MOAN**?

KEEP GOING

Three of these four words are written in number code.

The codes are **not** written in the same order as the words and one of the codes is missing.

WEST   TOES   STEW   STOW

2431   4532   1324

Work out the correct code for each word and answer the following questions.

Mark the correct answer on the answer sheet.

QUESTION **78**

Which word has the number code **2451**?

QUESTION **79**

What is the code for the word **WETS**?

QUESTION **80**

What is the code for the word **SEWS**?

END OF TEST 5

Paper 6

In these questions, find a letter that will complete the word in front of the brackets and begin the word after the brackets.
You must use the **same** letter in **both** sets of brackets.

Example

tra   (?)   et
man   (?)   es

Answer

y   (the four words are
     tray, yet, many, yes)

QUESTION **1**

rea   (?)   ump
fur   (?)   int

QUESTION **2**

pin   (?)   ill
lin   (?)   iln

QUESTION **3**

cal   (?)   ite
fil   (?)   ark

QUESTION **4**

lam   (?)   ray
com   (?)   ury

QUESTION **5**

bea   (?)   ay
bee   (?)   ash

QUESTION **6**

fea   (?)   ide
las   (?)   int

QUESTION **7**

hi   (?)   oll
ski   (?)   lay

KEEP GOING

In the following questions, take a letter from the first word and move it into the second word to form two new words.
All the other letters must stay in the same order and both new words must make sense.

Work out which letter moves and mark it on the answer sheet.

Example

heart   camp

Answer

r   (the two new words are
     heat and **cramp**)

QUESTION **8**

spurt   moor

QUESTION **9**

prism   duty

QUESTION **10**

plank   our

QUESTION **11**

tiled   word

QUESTION **12**

bread   fury

QUESTION **13**

flour   caste

QUESTION **14**

cover   petty

GO STRAIGHT ON

A B C D E F G H I J K L M N O P Q R S T U V W X Y Z

The alphabet is here to help you with the following questions. Work out which pair of letters will come next in the sequence and mark your answer on the answer sheet.

Example

       AZ is to **BY**
       as
       CX is to [?]

Answer

          DW

QUESTION **15**

DL is to **HI**
as
MN is to [?]

QUESTION **16**

XC is to **TH**
as
PA is to [?]

QUESTION **17**

WT is to **BY**
as
LR is to [?]

QUESTION **18**

JZ is to **DD**
as
KL is to [?]

QUESTION **19**

EB is to **ZY**
as
GO is to [?]

KEEP GOING

QUESTION **20**

GG is to **JB**
as
HH is to [?]

QUESTION **21**

NX is to **UD**
as
YO is to [?]

Read the following information, then work out the correct answer to the question and mark its letter on the answer sheet.

QUESTION **22**

Oliver took 8 sweets out of a jar containing 100. Rebecca took three times as many as Harry who took 4 more than Oliver but 5 less than Sophie. Oliver took 6 less than Jenny.

How many sweets were left in the jar?

A. 37

B. 49

C. 25

D. 13

E. 18

GO STRAIGHT ON

13

In the following questions, find **two** words, one from each row, that are **most opposite in meaning.**

Example

(borrow   buy   sell)
(purchase   own   lend)

Answer

borrow   lend

QUESTION 23

(outside   superior   exterior)
(external   outstanding   inferior)

QUESTION 24

(squander   lose   donate)
(waste   hoard   tight)

QUESTION 25

(replicate   cheat   salivate)
(copy   delegate   originate)

QUESTION 26

(justice   trivial   attempt)
(important   pursuit   trial)

QUESTION 27

(coarse   penalty   duty)
(rough   fine   course)

QUESTION 28

(vague   transparent   unclear)
(dim   opaque   dark)

QUESTION 29

(poverty   property   money)
(cash   wealth   health)

QUESTION 30

(loiter   scurry   scramble)
(beat   hasten   detour)

KEEP GOING

In the following series, find the number which comes next in the most sensible way, and mark it on the answer sheet.

Example

1   3   5   7   [?]

Answer

9

QUESTION 31

1   6   10   13   15   [?]

QUESTION 32

9   7   5.5   4.5   4   [?]

QUESTION 33

47   29   18   11   7   4   [?]

QUESTION 34

5   10   8   13   11   [?]

QUESTION 35

4   3.25   2.5   1.75   1   [?]

QUESTION 36

2   4   6   12   14   [?]

QUESTION 37

36   18   16   8   6   [?]

GO STRAIGHT ON

In each sentence there is a word of **four** letters hidden between the end of one word and the beginning of the next.

Find the pair of words that contains the hidden word and mark your answer on the answer sheet.

Example

He skis so badly.

Answer

skis so (the hidden word is **kiss**)

QUESTION **38**

The school trip ended in disaster!

QUESTION **39**

Remember to give in your essays.

QUESTION **40**

He irritates her when he whistles.

QUESTION **41**

Her train took hours to arrive.

QUESTION **42**

The surgery shuts on certain days.

QUESTION **43**

The weather was perfect last April.

QUESTION **44**

Each show lasts over three hours.

KEEP GOING

Read the following information, then work out the correct answer to the question and mark it on the answer sheet.

QUESTION **45**

Vijay is taller than Claire.
Vishnu is shorter than Henry.
Vijay is taller than Amelia.
Vishnu and Vijay are the same height.

Who is the tallest?

a. Claire

b. Henry

c. Vijay

d. Amelia

e. Vishnu

In each of the following questions, there is the same relationship between the word outside the brackets and a word inside each set of brackets.
Choose **two** words, one from each set of brackets, that complete the sentence in the best way.

Example

cat is to
(tiger   kitten   calf)

as **dog** is to
(bone   kennel   puppy)

Answer

kitten   puppy

QUESTION **46**

birth is to
(life   death   cradle)

as **source** is to
(gravy   terminus   ketchup)

KEEP GOING

15

QUESTION **47**

flute is to
(gale   breeze   wind)

as **cello** is to
(string   rope   twine)

QUESTION **48**

clock is to
(alarm   finger   hand)

as **compass** is to
(north   direction   needle)

QUESTION **49**

coal is to
(solid   mine   warm)

as **oil** is to
(fry   yours   well)

QUESTION **50**

banana is to
(yellow   fruit   skin)

as **egg** is to
(yolk   shell   boiled)

QUESTION **51**

comic is to
(read   magazine   laugh)

as **tragic** is to
(sad   novel   cry)

QUESTION **52**

water is to
(shower   ice   swim)

as **rain** is to
(umbrella   wet   hail)

GO STRAIGHT ON

A B C D E F G H I J K L M N O P Q R S T U V W X Y Z

The alphabet is here to help you with the following questions. There is a different code for each question. Find the correct answer and mark it on the answer sheet.

Example
If the code for **HARD** is **IBSE**, what does **UFTU** mean?

Answer   **TEST**

QUESTION **53**

If the code for **WATCH** is **AXVZL**, what is the code for **CLOCK**?

QUESTION **54**

If the code for **TOAST** is **PLYPP**, what does **XBYKO** mean?

QUESTION **55**

If the code for **DANCE** is **CBMDD**, what is the code for **TANGO**?

QUESTION **56**

If the code for **STAIR** is **RRXEM**, what does **SPBWY** mean?

QUESTION **57**

If the code for **DENIM** is **FHRLO**, what is the code for **SKIRT**?

QUESTION **58**

If the code for **FRUIT** is **IOXFW**, what does **SBDZK** mean?

QUESTION **59**

If the code for **STAG** is **PWXJ**, what is the code for **DEER**?

GO STRAIGHT ON

In each question there are two pairs of words.
Only **one** of the answers will go equally
well with **both** pairs of words.
Mark **one** word on the answer sheet.

Example

      (just   reasonable)
      (blonde   light)

Answer
          fair

QUESTION **60**

(licence   warrant)
(allow   consent)

QUESTION **61**

(ringlet   curl)
(bolt   secure)

QUESTION **62**

(cease   halt)
(rest   remain)

QUESTION **63**

(manicure   sharpen)
(document folder)

QUESTION **64**

(neat   dapper)
(fir   pine)

QUESTION **65**

(gate   doorway)
(charm   fascinate)

QUESTION **66**

(implement cutlery)
(turn   veer)

KEEP GOING

In the following questions, the three numbers
in **each** group are related in the **same** way.

Find the number which belongs with the last
group and mark it on the answer sheet.

Example

    (2 [6] 3)   (4 [8] 2)

        (5 [?] 3)

Answer

          15

QUESTION **67**

(4 [6] 3)   (3 [9] 6)

     (5 [?] 6)

QUESTION **68**

(4 [22] 7)   (12 [42] 9)

     (6 [?] 7)

QUESTION **69**

(40 [30] 20)   (16 [12] 8)

     (20 [?] 6)

QUESTION **70**

(16 [12] 3)   (49 [14] 2)

     (100 [?] 3)

QUESTION **71**

(10 [14] 2)   (6 [12] 3)

     (4 [?] 4)

GO STRAIGHT ON

QUESTION **72**

(6 [14] 8)   (10 [22] 12)

(14 [?] 16)

QUESTION **73**

(5 [7] 9)   (8 [10] 12)

(11 [?] 15)

QUESTION **74**

(48 [16] 6)   (36 [6] 12)

(28 [?] 7)

KEEP GOING

Each question below contains three pairs of words.

Find the word that completes the last pair of words in the **same way** as the other two pairs.

Mark your answer on the answer sheet.

Example

(three   the)   (shame   she)
(bacon   [?   ])

Answer

ban

QUESTION **75**

(play   pray)   (bland   brand)
(clamp   [?   ])

QUESTION **76**

(between   went)   (catcher   cart)
(verbena   [?   ])

QUESTION **77**

(malt   melt)   (lent   lint)
(pile   [?   ])

QUESTION **78**

(bandit   bait)   (tipped   tied)
(mangle   [?   ])

QUESTION **79**

(east   feast)   (our   pour)
(ark   [?   ])

QUESTION **80**

(prayer   year)   (crater   tear)
(healed   [?   ])

END OF TEST 6

MULTIPLE CHOICE ANSWER SHEET 5

**Please mark your answers with a single line
from side to side across the box** ▭

Do not mark outside the boxes

AMPLE
- e ▬
- he ☐
- ve ☐
- am ☐
- at ▬
- are ☐

1
- pat ☐
- cot ☐
- ever ☐
- one ☐
- age ☐
- ton ☐

2
- tap ☐
- use ☐
- peas ☐
- sing ☐
- full ☐
- ant ☐

3
- car ☐
- he ☐
- are ☐
- pit ☐
- rear ☐
- art ☐

AMPLE
- ar ☐
- lum ☐
- t ☐
- our ☐
- am ☐
- age ☐

5
- pup ☐
- can ☐
- ape ☐
- pit ☐
- ear ☐
- did ☐

6
- miss ☐
- disc ☐
- tape ☐
- cord ☐
- lame ☐
- over ☐

7
- plain ☐
- neck ☐
- at ☐
- tack ☐
- lass ☐
- tick ☐

AMPLE
- h ☐
- e ☐
- a ☐
- r ▬
- t ☐

8
- s ☐
- t ☐
- a ☐
- n ☐
- d ☐

9
- r ☐
- e ☐
- g ☐
- a ☐
- l ☐

10
- q ☐
- u ☐
- i ☐
- e ☐
- t ☐

11
- t ☐
- a ☐
- b ☐
- l ☐
- e ☐

12
- b ☐
- e ☐
- l ☐
- o ☐
- w ☐

13
- s ☐
- n ☐
- o ☐
- r ☐
- e ☐

14
- f ☐
- i ☐
- e ☐
- n ☐
- d ☐

AMPLE
- A ☐
- B ☐
- C ☐
- D ▬
- E ☐

15
- A ☐
- B ☐
- C ☐
- D ☐
- E ☐

16
- A ☐
- B ☐
- C ☐
- D ☐
- E ☐

17
- A ☐
- B ☐
- C ☐
- D ☐
- E ☐

18
- A ☐
- B ☐
- C ☐
- D ☐
- E ☐

19
- A ☐
- B ☐
- C ☐
- D ☐
- E ☐

20
- A ☐
- B ☐
- C ☐
- D ☐
- E ☐

21
- A ☐
- B ☐
- C ☐
- D ☐
- E ☐

22
- a ☐
- b ☐
- c ☐
- d ☐
- e ☐

AMPLE
- He skis ☐
- skis so ▬
- so badly. ☐

23
- The car ☐
- car engine ☐
- engine made ☐
- made strange ☐
- strange noises. ☐

24
- My dog ☐
- dog really ☐
- really enjoys ☐
- enjoys his ☐
- his food ☐

25
- We admit ☐
- admit children ☐
- children accompanied ☐
- accompanied by ☐
- by adults. ☐

26
- Why do ☐
- do men ☐
- men love ☐
- love computer ☐
- computer games? ☐

- Go left ☐
- left at ☐
- at the ☐
- the next ☐
- next roundabout. ☐

28
- Who made ☐
- made these ☐
- these delicious ☐
- delicious jam ☐
- jam tarts? ☐

29
- The games ☐
- games start ☐
- start punctually ☐
- punctually at ☐
- at eight. ☐

30
- You are ☐
- are not ☐
- not allowed ☐
- allowed to ☐
- to swear. ☐

XAMPLE
- carrot ☐
- turnip ☐
- mango ▬
- pea ☐
- apple ▬

31
- vacant ☐
- plain ☐
- simple ☐
- empty ☐
- unadorned ☐

32
- barley ☐
- oats ☐
- mint ☐
- parsley ☐
- wheat ☐

33
- hazard ☐
- sanctuary ☐
- peril ☐
- danger ☐
- safety ☐

34
- herring ☐
- cod ☐
- lobster ☐
- sole ☐
- crab ☐

35
- elm ☐
- poplar ☐
- friendly ☐
- birch ☐
- sociable ☐

36
- hoax ☐
- trick ☐
- entice ☐
- persuade ☐
- coax ☐

37
- granite ☐
- platinum ☐
- silver ☐
- marble ☐
- gold ☐

PLEASE TURN OVER THE PAGE

EXAMPLE			
scent	▬	bottle	☐
glass	☐	liquid	☐
fragrant	☐	odour	▬

38
rehearsed	☐	acted	☐
play	☐	practised	☐
theatre	☐	danced	☐

39
tough	☐	tender	☐
valiant	☐	lean	☐
vigorous	☐	courageous	☐

40
orange	☐	heart	☐
pip	☐	apple	☐
core	☐	peel	☐

41
quiet	☐	exam	☐
din	☐	pass	☐
study	☐	noise	☐

42
follow	☐	lead	☐
enter	☐	outcome	☐
consequence	☐	exit	☐

43
height	☐	bottom	☐
top	☐	width	☐
aptitude	☐	altitude	☐

44
recount	☐	number	☐
family	☐	figure	☐
square	☐	relate	☐

45
strike	☐	coconut	☐
shy	☐	stable	☐
hit	☐	bashful	☐

EXAMPLE
1	☐
2	☐
3	▬
4	☐
5	☐

46
3	☐
4	☐
5	☐
6	☐
7	☐

47
3	☐
4	☐
5	☐
6	☐
7	☐

48
1	☐
2	☐
3	☐
4	☐
5	☐

49
6	☐
7	☐
8	☐
9	☐
10	☐

50
20	☐
25	☐
28	☐
30	☐
32	☐

51
3	☐
4	☐
5	☐
6	☐
7	☐

52
8	☐
10	☐
12	☐
14	☐
16	☐

53
a	☐
b	☐
c	☐
d	☐
e	☐

EXAMPLE
HER	☐
ROW	▬
HIM	☐
RAT	☐
LOW	☐

54
OWL	☐
IRE	☐
OUR	☐
EAR	☐
ARM	☐

55
TUB	☐
OWL	☐
ROW	☐
LOW	☐
COB	☐

56
PET	☐
ACT	☐
PIT	☐
ART	☐
ERA	☐

57
TAR	☐
RAT	☐
EAR	☐
ART	☐
ORE	☐

58
POT	☐
PET	☐
PIT	☐
PAT	☐
MET	☐

59
HAD	☐
AND	☐
TEA	☐
PAD	☐
MUD	☐

60
MAR	☐
PIT	☐
BAT	☐
BUT	☐
COT	☐

EXAMPLE
can	☐
con	☐
cob	☐
ban	▬
cab	☐

61
ban	☐
ran	☐
can	☐
cab	☐
bar	☐

62
seat	☐
seal	☐
ales	☐
sine	☐
sane	☐

63
pane	☐
pine	☐
oven	☐
open	☐
aped	☐

64
mast	☐
matt	☐
mats	☐
mess	☐
arms	☐

65
made	☐
mead	☐
pend	☐
dame	☐
damp	☐

66
fired	☐
fiery	☐
fires	☐
fries	☐
fibre	☐

67
seal	☐
late	☐
seat	☐
lest	☐
slat	☐

EXAMPLE
QT	☐
PT	▬
QS	☐
OT	☐
OS	☐

68
DO	☐
OE	☐
OD	☐
MD	☐
ME	☐

69
ZM	☐
LY	☐
YM	☐
YO	☐
YL	☐

70
ZK	☐
ZL	☐
LK	☐
YK	☐
YL	☐

71
PS	☐
PQ	☐
QR	☐
PR	☐
RP	☐

72
MO	☐
NO	☐
OO	☐
ML	☐
MP	☐

73
EK	☐
EJ	☐
FJ	☐
FK	☐
JK	☐

74
VE	☐
VF	☐
WE	☐
WF	☐
XF	☐

75
MEAT	☐
MOON	☐
MOAN	☐
MEAN	☐
MEET	☐

76
4132	☐
4613	☐
4631	☐
4651	☐
5631	☐

77
1563	☐
1625	☐
3265	☐
3652	☐
5632	☐

78
WEST	☐
TOES	☐
STEW	☐
STOW	☐
TOWS	☐

79
4532	☐
2431	☐
3124	☐
1324	☐
1342	☐

80
2312	☐
2321	☐
2154	☐
2345	☐
2451	☐

END OF TEST 5

MULTIPLE CHOICE ANSWER SHEET 6

**Please mark your answers with a single line
from side to side across the box** ▭

Do not mark outside the boxes

SAMPLE
- m ▭
- t ▭
- p ▭
- d ▭
- y ▬

1
- d ▭
- l ▭
- m ▭
- p ▭
- r ▭

2
- d ▭
- t ▭
- n ▭
- p ▭
- k ▭

3
- b ▭
- k ▭
- m ▭
- p ▭
- t ▭

4
- p ▭
- d ▭
- e ▭
- b ▭
- t ▭

5
- m ▭
- d ▭
- f ▭
- k ▭
- r ▭

6
- k ▭
- l ▭
- r ▭
- s ▭
- t ▭

7
- d ▭
- m ▭
- p ▭
- s ▭
- t ▭

SAMPLE
- h ▭
- e ▭
- a ▭
- r ▬
- t ▭

8
- s ▭
- p ▭
- u ▭
- r ▭
- t ▭

9
- p ▭
- r ▭
- i ▭
- s ▭
- m ▭

10
- p ▭
- l ▭
- a ▭
- n ▭
- k ▭

11
- t ▭
- i ▭
- l ▭
- e ▭
- d ▭

12
- b ▭
- r ▭
- e ▭
- a ▭
- d ▭

13
- f ▭
- l ▭
- o ▭
- u ▭
- r ▭

14
- c ▭
- o ▭
- v ▭
- e ▭
- r ▭

SAMPLE
- WD ▭
- BW ▭
- BY ▭
- DW ▬
- YB ▭

15
- KQ ▭
- LQ ▭
- QK ▭
- QL ▭
- QQ ▭

16
- LF ▭
- LG ▭
- MG ▭
- TF ▭
- TG ▭

17
- GW ▭
- GX ▭
- WQ ▭
- QW ▭
- QX ▭

18
- CH ▭
- DH ▭
- EP ▭
- QO ▭
- QP ▭

19
- AD ▭
- BD ▭
- BL ▭
- BR ▭
- JL ▭

20
- CK ▭
- KC ▭
- KF ▭
- KL ▭
- LK ▭

21
- EH ▭
- FH ▭
- FI ▭
- FU ▭
- FT ▭

22
- A ▭
- B ▭
- C ▭
- D ▭
- E ▭

SAMPLE
borrow	▬	purchase	▭
buy	▭	own	▭
sell	▭	lend	▬

23
outside	▭	external	▭
superior	▭	outstanding	▭
exterior	▭	inferior	▭

24
squander	▭	waste	▭
lose	▭	hoard	▭
donate	▭	tight	▭

25
replicate	▭	copy	▭
cheat	▭	delegate	▭
salivate	▭	originate	▭

justice	▭	important	▭
trivial	▭	pursuit	▭
attempt	▭	trial	▭

27
coarse	▭	rough	▭
penalty	▭	fine	▭
duty	▭	course	▭

28
vague	▭	dim	▭
transparent	▭	opaque	▭
unclear	▭	dark	▭

29
poverty	▭	cash	▭
property	▭	wealth	▭
money	▭	health	▭

loiter	▭	beat	▭
scurry	▭	hasten	▭
scramble	▭	detour	▭

EXAMPLE
- 6 ▭
- 7 ▭
- 8 ▭
- 9 ▬
- 10 ▭

31
- 14 ▭
- 15 ▭
- 16 ▭
- 17 ▭
- 18 ▭

32
- 2 ▭
- 3 ▭
- 3.5 ▭
- 4 ▭
- 4.5 ▭

33
- 0 ▭
- 1 ▭
- 2 ▭
- 3 ▭
- 4 ▭

34
- 14 ▭
- 15 ▭
- 16 ▭
- 17 ▭
- 18 ▭

35
- 1 ▭
- 0.75 ▭
- 0.50 ▭
- 0.25 ▭
- 0.12 ▭

36
- 16 ▭
- 18 ▭
- 20 ▭
- 28 ▭
- 30 ▭

37
- 1 ▭
- 2 ▭
- 3 ▭
- 4 ▭
- 5 ▭

PLEASE TURN OVER THE PAGE

EXAMPLE

He skis ☐
skis so ▬
so badly. ☐

38
The school ☐
school trip ☐
trip ended ☐
ended in ☐
in disaster. ☐

39
Remember to ☐
to give ☐
give in ☐
in your ☐
your essays. ☐

40
He irritates ☐
irritates her ☐
her when ☐
when he ☐
he whistles. ☐

41
Her train ☐
train took ☐
took hours ☐
hours to ☐
to arrive. ☐

42
The surgery ☐
surgery shuts ☐
shuts on ☐
on certain ☐
certain days. ☐

43
The weather ☐
weather was ☐
was perfect ☐
perfect last ☐
last April. ☐

44
Each show ☐
show lasts ☐
lasts over ☐
over three ☐
three hours. ☐

45
a ☐
b ☐
c ☐
d ☐
e ☐

EXAMPLE

tiger ☐   bone ☐
kitten ▬   kennel ☐
calf ☐   puppy ▬

46
life ☐   gravy ☐
death ☐   terminus ☐
cradle ☐   ketchup ☐

47
gale ☐   string ☐
breeze ☐   rope ☐
wind ☐   twine ☐

48
alarm ☐   north ☐
finger ☐   direction ☐
hand ☐   needle ☐

49
solid ☐   fry ☐
mine ☐   yours ☐
warm ☐   well ☐

50
yellow ☐   yolk ☐
fruit ☐   shell ☐
skin ☐   boiled ☐

51
read ☐   sad ☐
magazine ☐   novel ☐
laugh ☐   cry ☐

52
shower ☐   umbrella ☐
ice ☐   wet ☐
swim ☐   hail ☐

EXAMPLE

WETS ☐
VETS ☐
VEST ☐
TEST ▬
WEST ☐

53
GIQAO ☐
GIQZO ☐
GOQZO ☐
YHLFN ☐
YOMEF ☐

54
BEADS ☐
BEARD ☐
BEANS ☐
BEARS ☐
BEAST ☐

55
SBLHN ☐
SBMHN ☐
SBOHN ☐
UZOFP ☐
UZNFP ☐

56
TRACE ☐
TRADE ☐
TREAD ☐
TREND ☐
TREAT ☐

57
CBJEK ☐
QHEOR ☐
TMLTU ☐
UMLSU ☐
UNMUV ☐

58
PEACE ☐
PEACH ☐
PEALS ☐
PEARS ☐
PERCH ☐

59
ABBU ☐
AHBO ☐
AHBU ☐
GAHO ☐
GBHO ☐

EXAMPLE

fair ▬
party ☐
fete ☐
festival ☐
rave ☐

60
deny ☐
fight ☐
paper ☐
permit ☐
right ☐

61
bun ☐
cut ☐
key ☐
lock ☐
run ☐

62
depart ☐
drift ☐
leave ☐
point ☐
stop ☐

63
book ☐
envelope ☐
file ☐
nail ☐
note ☐

64
fine ☐
pine ☐
spruce ☐
tidy ☐
willow ☐

65
delight ☐
entrance ☐
portal ☐
spell ☐
trick ☐

66
bend ☐
curve ☐
knife ☐
fork ☐
spoon ☐

EXAMPLE

4 ☐
5 ☐
10 ☐
15 ▬
20 ☐

67
10 ☐
11 ☐
15 ☐
22 ☐
30 ☐

68
13 ☐
15 ☐
24 ☐
26 ☐
42 ☐

69
13 ☐
14 ☐
16 ☐
26 ☐
32 ☐

70
13 ☐
16 ☐
26 ☐
30 ☐
33 ☐

71
10 ☐
12 ☐
14 ☐
18 ☐
20 ☐

72
20 ☐
30 ☐
40 ☐
50 ☐
60 ☐

73
12 ☐
13 ☐
14 ☐
15 ☐
26 ☐

74
2 ☐
4 ☐
8 ☐
16 ☐
18 ☐

EXAMPLE

can ☐
con ☐
cob ☐
ban ▬
cab ☐

75
champ ☐
chart ☐
cramp ☐
crams ☐
crate ☐

76
bear ☐
beat ☐
beer ☐
veer ☐
vest ☐

77
pail ☐
pale ☐
pile ☐
pole ☐
polo ☐

78
mane ☐
male ☐
mile ☐
mole ☐
mule ☐

79
bark ☐
dark ☐
hark ☐
lark ☐
mark ☐

80
deal ☐
hale ☐
head ☐
heal ☐
lead ☐

END OF TEST 6

MULTIPLE CHOICE ANSWER SHEET 7

**Please mark your answers with a single line
from side to side across the box** ▭

Do not mark outside the boxes

EXAMPLE
- He skis ▭
- skis so ▬
- so badly ▭

1
- You might ▭
- might win ▭
- win our ▭
- our top ▭
- top prize! ▭

2
- His little ▭
- little sister ▭
- sister cries ▭
- cries all ▭
- all night. ▭

3
- After many ▭
- many attempts ▭
- attempts he ▭
- he finally ▭
- finally won. ▭

4
- It was ▭
- was late ▭
- late when ▭
- when they ▭
- they arrived. ▭

- The conjuror ▭
- conjuror entertained ▭
- entertained the ▭
- the lucky ▭
- lucky children. ▭

6
- They escaped ▭
- escaped under ▭
- under the ▭
- the wire ▭
- wire fence. ▭

7
- Remember to ▭
- to water ▭
- water the ▭
- the garden ▭
- garden tonight. ▭

EXAMPLE
- m ▭
- t ▭
- p ▭
- d ▭
- y ▬

8
- d ▭
- l ▭
- n ▭
- s ▭
- t ▭

9
- t ▭
- e ▭
- o ▭
- b ▭
- y ▭

10
- b ▭
- r ▭
- t ▭
- v ▭
- w ▭

11
- d ▭
- g ▭
- m ▭
- p ▭
- t ▭

12
- p ▭
- d ▭
- b ▭
- r ▭
- t ▭

13
- d ▭
- f ▭
- l ▭
- p ▭
- t ▭

14
- b ▭
- h ▭
- n ▭
- p ▭
- w ▭

EXAMPLE
- A ▭
- B ▭
- C ▭
- D ▬
- E ▭

15
- A ▭
- B ▭
- C ▭
- D ▭
- E ▭

16
- A ▭
- B ▭
- C ▭
- D ▭
- E ▭

17
- A ▭
- B ▭
- C ▭
- D ▭
- E ▭

18
- A ▭
- B ▭
- C ▭
- D ▭
- E ▭

19
- A ▭
- B ▭
- C ▭
- D ▭
- E ▭

20
- A ▭
- B ▭
- C ▭
- D ▭
- E ▭

21
- A ▭
- B ▭
- C ▭
- D ▭
- E ▭

22
- a ▭
- b ▭
- c ▭
- d ▭
- e ▭

EXAMPLE
- scent ▬   bottle ▭
- glass ▭   liquid ▭
- fragrant ▭   odour ▬

23
- programme ▭   radio ▭
- vision ▭   television ▭
- sound ▭   foresight ▭

24
- infectious ▭   disease ▭
- cold ▭   serious ▭
- malicious ▭   contagious ▭

25
- friend ▭   enemy ▭
- passage ▭   ally ▭
- warrior ▭   package ▭

- render ▭   surrender ▭
- loose ▭   gain ▭
- capitulate ▭   decapitate ▭

27
- dirty ▭   clean ▭
- gravel ▭   pristine ▭
- speckled ▭   soiled ▭

28
- quick ▭   short ▭
- tedious ▭   eternal ▭
- everlasting ▭   current ▭

29
- decline ▭   receive ▭
- tolerate ▭   give ▭
- refuse ▭   accept ▭

EXAMPLE
- HER ▭
- ROW ▬
- HIM ▭
- RAT ▭
- LOW ▭

30
- LAD ▭
- LED ▭
- MAT ▭
- MET ▭
- PIT ▭

31
- EAT ▭
- HIS ▭
- NET ▭
- RAT ▭
- WIT ▭

32
- ATE ▭
- CUE ▭
- EWE ▭
- HAD ▭
- HOW ▭

33
- ARE ▭
- HIM ▭
- LEG ▭
- OUR ▭
- RAT ▭

34
- SON ▭
- TAN ▭
- TIN ▭
- SIN ▭
- TON ▭

35
- BUT ▭
- FAN ▭
- BIT ▭
- FIN ▭
- OUR ▭

36
- SIN ▭
- SON ▭
- SUN ▭
- TEN ▭
- TIN ▭

PLEASE TURN OVER THE PAGE

EXAMPLE			
can	☐		
con	☐		
cob	☐		
ban	▬		
cab	☐		

37
logo	☐
look	☐
loom	☐
loop	☐
loot	☐

38
lead	☐
lame	☐
lamb	☐
male	☐
meal	☐

39
wind	☐
wide	☐
wane	☐
wand	☐
wade	☐

40
earl	☐
ears	☐
laps	☐
leap	☐
slap	☐

41
clues	☐
clown	☐
cloud	☐
clean	☐
clear	☐

42
sale	☐
salt	☐
sate	☐
seal	☐
seat	☐

43
swinger	
splints	
stinger	
stinted	
stringy	

EXAMPLE			
he	▬	am	☐
she	☐	at	▬
we	☐	are	☐

44
deed	☐	my	☐
feat	☐	him	☐
do	☐	her	☐

45
did	☐	eat	☐
den	☐	ate	☐
don	☐	tall	☐

46
torn	☐	it	☐
rip	☐	era	☐
war	☐	ado	☐

47
do	☐	rain	☐
for	☐	tempt	☐
at	☐	trick	☐

48
book	☐	set	☐
page	☐	king	☐
note	☐	ant	☐

49
neat	☐	err	☐
tidy	☐	ate	☐
prim	☐	eat	☐

50
go	☐	rest	☐
leave	☐	dies	☐
come	☐	less	☐

51
bar	☐	done	☐
car	☐	ties	☐
par	☐	rent	☐

EXAMPLE	
2	☐
3	☐
4	▬
6	☐
12	☐

52
5	☐
6	☐
7	☐
8	☐
9	☐

53
8	☐
9	☐
11	☐
12	☐
13	☐

54
1	☐
2	☐
3	☐
4	☐
7	☐

55
5	☐
6	☐
7	☐
8	☐
9	☐

56
1	☐
2	☐
3	☐
4	☐
5	☐

57
4	☐
5	☐
6	☐
7	☐
8	☐

58
64	☐
72	☐
84	☐
96	☐
108	☐

EXAMPLE	
carrot	☐
turnip	☐
mango	▬
pea	☐
apple	▬

59
wet	☐
moist	☐
damp	☐
tepid	☐
cool	☐

60
sultana	☐
current	☐
fruit	☐
raisin	☐
prune	☐

61
trawler	☐
vessel	☐
barge	☐
canoe	☐
oar	☐

62
uncle	☐
nephew	☐
lass	☐
farther	☐
son	☐

63
oboe	☐
flute	☐
guitar	☐
piano	☐
clarinet	☐

64
peel	☐
area	☐
rind	☐
acne	☐
skin	☐

65
decrease	☐
minimize	☐
lesson	☐
extend	☐
shorten	☐

66
rarely	☐
constantly	☐
infrequently	☐
seldom	☐
often	☐

67
a	☐
b	☐
c	☐
d	☐
e	☐

EXAMPLE	
QT	☐
PT	▬
QS	☐
OT	☐
OS	☐

68
RE	☐
RF	☐
SE	☐
SF	☐
SG	☐

69
IE	☐
IF	☐
ID	☐
MD	☐
ND	☐

70
VO	☐
VP	☐
WO	☐
WP	☐
XP	☐

71
PX	☐
PZ	☐
RU	☐
RV	☐
IJ	☐

72
SG	☐
SF	☐
RG	☐
GF	☐
FG	☐

73
HK	
HL	
IK	
IL	
IM	

74
TW	☐
TX	☐
VW	☐
VJ	☐
XW	☐

75
MOON	☐
MOOD	☐
NODE	☐
DONE	☐
MODE	☐

76
1332	☐
1553	☐
1552	☐
2331	☐
3224	☐

77
3224	☐
3441	☐
1443	☐
4331	☐
4225	☐

78
AMBER	☐
BREAM	☐
DREAD	☐
DARED	☐
DREAM	☐

79
4216	
4142	
6415	
6142	
2456	

80
6412	☐
2456	☐
6142	☐
4215	☐
6124	☐

END OF TEST 7

MULTIPLE CHOICE ANSWER SHEET 8

**Please mark your answers with a single line
from side to side across the box** ▭

Do not mark outside the boxes

EXAMPLE
h
e
a
r
t

1
b
l
a
n
k

2
t
h
u
m
p

3
m
o
i
s
t

4
f
r
a
m
e

5
t
a
b
l
e

6
c
h
o
r
d

7
c
h
e
a
t

EXAMPLE
m
t
p
d
y

8
k
n
p
t
y

9
l
m
p
t
w

10
d
e
g
k
t

11
d
g
n
t
y

12
b
g
n
r
y

13
e
t
f
l
d

14
u
o
t
e
y

15
d
n
p
r
y

EXAMPLE
WD
BW
BY
DW
YB

16
EF
FI
PF
JF
OF

17
FT
FZ
TF
TX
XT

18
LQ
LR
QR
RQ
RR

19
JL
JV
KL
KV
LV

20
TE
TF
TG
TZ
ZF

21
HF
HG
IF
JF
JG

22
BW
BY
CI
CW
CY

23
a
b
c
d
e

EXAMPLE
He skis
skis so
so badly.

24
Play a
a tune
tune on
on the
the piano.

25
Peter left
left a
a little
little after
after six.

26
Our old
old horse
horse attempted
attempted a
a jump.

27
Everyone was
was invited
invited to
to the
the picnic.

None of
of our
our family
family is
is lucky.

29
Remember to
to sign
sign at
at the
the bottom.

30
They drink
drink nothing
nothing but
but diet
diet cola.

31
a
b
c
d
e

EXAMPLE
tiger · bone
kitten · kennel
calf · puppy

32
bottle · heavy
lid · metal
float · sink

33
driver · window
petrol · garden
vehicle · residence

34
slope · harsh
merciful · animal
wobble · thrash

beat · turn
swing · plane
hit · strike

36
hear · sense
touch · see
say · smell

37
still · phone
train · moving
paper · energetic

38
beginning · coil
cold · start
end · leap

PLEASE TURN OVER THE PAGE

EXAMPLE		39		40		41		42		43		44		45	
WETS	☐	LXNBN	☐	BEGS	☐	FYOLI	☐	FENCE	☐	JBJL	☐	SELLS	☐	KLJCY	
VETS	☐	LXOBN	☐	BRAG	☐	FYOWI	☐	FIEND	☐	JBVL	☐	SLIDE	☐	KLRBV	
VEST	☐	MVQHV	☐	GAPS	☐	TKWEO	☐	FINCH	☐	JBLV	☐	SLIPS	☐	KLJBW	
TEST	▭	TDRBN	☐	GRAB	☐	TKYEO	☐	FINDS	☐	JVLB	☐	SLOPE	☐	ORRHA	
WEST	☐	TDRHV	☐	GARB	☐	TKYOE	☐	FINER	☐	ZTFR	☐	SMILE	☐	OLRBA	

EXAMPLE				46				47				48			
borrow	▭	purchase	☐	income	☐	arrive	☐	indolent	☐	lazy	☐	vital	☐	water	
buy	☐	own	☐	check	☐	expenditure	☐	industrious	☐	insolent	☐	essence	☐	fluid	
sell	☐	lend	▭	purchase	☐	cash	☐	idle	☐	cheeky	☐	liquid	☐	unessential	

49				50				51				52			
fine	☐	blame	☐	abundant	☐	scarce	☐	water	☐	fertile	☐	victory	☐	defeat	
pay	☐	penalize	☐	keen	☐	plentiful	☐	field	☐	dessert	☐	battle	☐	fight	
reward	☐	lose	☐	neat	☐	tidy	☐	barren	☐	paddock	☐	loose	☐	win	

EXAMPLE		53		54		55		56		57		58		59	
6	☐	0	☐	20	☐	12	☐	20	☐	30	☐	30	☐	34	
7	☐	1	☐	21	☐	13	☐	32	☐	32	☐	40	☐	36	
8	☐	2	☐	22	☐	14	☐	36	☐	36	☐	42	☐	38	
9	▭	3	☐	23	☐	15	☐	40	☐	38	☐	45	☐	40	
10	☐	4	☐	24	☐	16	☐	42	☐	40	☐	48	☐	42	

EXAMPLE		60		61		62		63		64		65		66	
fair	▭	car	☐	balance	☐	belt	☐	jewel	☐	citrus	☐	dim	☐	agree	
party	☐	coach	☐	leave	☐	contract	☐	magic	☐	cool	☐	drop	☐	arise	
fete	☐	engine	☐	left	☐	debate	☐	spell	☐	orange	☐	faint	☐	duty	
festival	☐	spot	☐	rock	☐	lessen	☐	charm	☐	bitter	☐	ill	☐	tie	
rave	☐	track	☐	wheels	☐	spoil	☐	clover	☐	snowy	☐	weak	☐	work	

EXAMPLE		67		68		69		70		71		72		73	
4	☐	4	☐	24	☐	11	☐	24	☐	24	☐	2	☐	4	
5	☐	6	☐	25	☐	12	☐	25	☐	26	☐	6	☐	6	
10	☐	8	☐	30	☐	13	☐	26	☐	27	☐	8	☐	16	
15	▭	10	☐	32	☐	14	☐	27	☐	31	☐	12	☐	20	
20	☐	12	☐	36	☐	15	☐	31	☐	36	☐	14	☐	32	

EXAMPLE		74		75		76		77		78		79		80	
cream	☐	meat	☐	belt	☐	err	☐	peal	☐	dense	☐	earl	☐	nags	
carat	☐	mate	☐	best	☐	ewe	☐	peel	☐	dress	☐	earn	☐	sags	
camel	▭	tame	☐	past	☐	fee	☐	peat	☐	drawn	☐	nail	☐	sign	
racer	☐	team	☐	sale	☐	foe	☐	seal	☐	water	☐	name	☐	sing	
trace	☐	tram	☐	stab	☐	for	☐	swap	☐	weeds	☐	neat	☐	wins	

END OF TEST 8

Paper 7

In each sentence there is a word of **four** letters hidden between the end of one word and the beginning of the next.

Find the pair of words that contains the hidden word and mark your answer on the answer sheet.

Example

He skis so badly.

Answer

skis so (the hidden word is **kiss**)

QUESTION **1**

You might win our top prize!

QUESTION **2**

His little sister cries all night.

QUESTION **3**

After many attempts he finally won.

QUESTION **4**

It was late when they arrived.

QUESTION **5**

The conjuror entertained the lucky children.

QUESTION **6**

They escaped under the wire fence.

QUESTION **7**

Remember to water the garden tonight.

KEEP GOING

In these questions, find a letter that will complete the word in front of the brackets and begin the word after the brackets. You must use the **same** letter in **both** sets of brackets.

Example

tra (?) et
man (?) es

Answer

y (the four words are **tray, yet, many, yes**)

QUESTION **8**

tow (?) ew
shi (?) one

QUESTION **9**

her (?) urn
cra (?) all

QUESTION **10**

ne (?) est
se (?) ant

QUESTION **11**

gri (?) ale
cur (?) urn

QUESTION **12**

cu (?) ow
blo (?) ind

QUESTION **13**

lea (?) ern
cal (?) ast

QUESTION **14**

so (?) arm
de (?) as

GO STRAIGHT ON

In these questions, letters represent numbers. Work out the answer to each sum, find its letter and mark it on the answer sheet.

Example

If   A=4,   B=3,   C=2,   D=6,   E=1,

what is the answer to this sum **as a letter**?

$$(B \times A) \div C = [\,?\,]$$

Answer

D

QUESTION **15**

If   A=6,   B=18,   C=12,   D=3,   E=36,

what is the answer to this sum **as a letter**?

$$(B - C) \times D = [\,?\,]$$

QUESTION **16**

If   A=3,   B=9,   C=4,   D=12,   E=6,

what is the answer to this sum **as a letter**?

$$(D \div C) \times A = [\,?\,]$$

QUESTION **17**

If   A=3,   B=8,   C=4,   D=12,   E=7,

what is the answer to this sum **as a letter**?

$$A (D - B) = [\,?\,]$$

QUESTION **18**

If   A=15,   B=6,   C=5,   D=2,   E=1,

what is the answer to this sum **as a letter**?

$$(B \times C) \div A = [\,?\,]$$

KEEP GOING

QUESTION **19**

If   A=2,   B=3,   C=4,   D=6,   E=12,

what is the answer to this sum **as a letter**?

$$(B \times C) \div D = [\,?\,]$$

QUESTION **20**

If   A=3,   B=4,   C=6,   D=12,   E=24,

what is the answer to this sum **as a letter**?

$$(E \div C) \times A = [\,?\,]$$

QUESTION **21**

If   A=2,   B=3,   C=5,   D=8,   E= 12,

what is the answer to this sum **as a letter**?

$$E + B - D = C + [\,?\,]$$

Read the following information, then work out the correct answer to the question and mark it on the answer sheet.

QUESTION **22**

Five minutes ago the town hall clock, which always tells the correct time, struck nine. My watch was then five minutes slow and three minutes later it stopped. When I arrived at school, the town hall clock showed 9.15.

What time did my watch show?

a.   8.55

b.   9.03

c.   9.10

d.   9.05

e.   8.58

GO STRAIGHT ON

Find **two** words, **one** from the top row and **one** from the bottom row, that are **closest in meaning**.

Mark **both** words on the answer sheet.

Example

(scent   glass   fragrant)
(bottle   liquid   odour)

Answer

scent   odour

QUESTION 23

(programme   vision   sound)
(radio   television   foresight)

QUESTION 24

(infectious   cold   malicious)
(disease   serious   contagious)

QUESTION 25

(friend   passage   warrior)
(enemy   ally   package)

QUESTION 26

(render   loose   capitulate)
(surrender   gain   decapitate)

QUESTION 27

(dirty   gravel   speckled)
(clean   pristine   soiled)

QUESTION 28

(quick   tedious   everlasting)
(short   eternal   current)

QUESTION 29

(decline   tolerate   refuse)
(receive   give   accept)

KEEP GOING

In each of the following sentences, **three letters next to each other** have been removed from the word in capitals.
These three letters make one correctly spelt word without changing their order.
Find the missing three letter word and mark it on the answer sheet.
The sentence must make sense.

Example

The cock **CED** loudly every morning.

Answer

ROW (The word in capitals is **CROWED**)

QUESTION 30

I often have **TOO** salad for lunch.

QUESTION 31

Don't touch that **TLE** as it will sting!

QUESTION 32

Rats lived in the **SRS** of the city.

QUESTION 33

The fans **ENCAGED** their team to score.

QUESTION 34

Please mind your own **BUESS**.

QUESTION 35

John is a very **AMIOUS** boy.

QUESTION 36

Competition for the gold medal was **INSE**.

GO STRAIGHT ON

Each question below contains three pairs of words.
Find the word that completes the last pair of words
in the **same way** as the other two pairs.

Mark your answer on the answer sheet.

Example

(three   the)   (shame   she)
(bacon   [?   ])

Answer

ban

QUESTION **37**

(rail   liar)   (evil   live)
(tool   [?   ])

QUESTION **38**

(please   leap)   (trendy   rent)
(blamed   [?   ])

QUESTION **39**

(bang   band)   (gone   done)
(wage   [?   ])

QUESTION **40**

(noodle   lone)   (liaise   sale)
(pearls   [?   ])

QUESTION **41**

(bar   bear)   (hard   heard)
(clan   [?   ])

QUESTION **42**

(passage   gasp)   (tenants   teat)
(tallest   [?   ])

QUESTION **43**

(pout   spouted)   (warm   swarmed)
(tint   [?   ])

In the following questions, find **one** word from the
top row and **one** word from the bottom row that
will join together to form **one** correctly spelt
new word.
The word from the top row always comes first.
Mark **both** words on the answer sheet.

Example

(he   she   we)
(am   at   are)

Answer

he   **at**   (the word is **heat**)

QUESTION **44**

(deed   feat   do)
(my   him   her)

QUESTION **45**

(did   den   don)
(eat   ate   tall)

QUESTION **46**

(torn   rip   war)
(it   era   ado)

QUESTION **47**

(do   for   at)
(rain   tempt   trick)

QUESTION **48**

(book   page   note)
(set   king   ant)

QUESTION **49**

(neat   tidy   prim)
(err   ate   eat)

QUESTION **50**

(go   leave   come)
(rest   dies   less)

QUESTION **51**

(bar   car   par)
(done   ties   rent)

KEEP GOING

GO STRAIGHT ON

23

In the following questions, find the number that will complete the sum correctly and mark it on the answer sheet.

Example

$$36 \div 3 = [\,?\,] \times 3$$

Answer

4

QUESTION **52**

$$41 - 13 = 4 \times [\,?\,]$$

QUESTION **53**

$$36 \times 2 = 6 \times [\,?\,]$$

QUESTION **54**

$$19 - 11 + 6 = 28 \div [\,?\,]$$

QUESTION **55**

$$(23 + 17) \div 8 = 45 \div [\,?\,]$$

QUESTION **56**

$$(132 \div 11) + 27 = 13 \times [\,?\,]$$

QUESTION **57**

$$(63 \div 3) \times 2 = 2 \times 3 \times [\,?\,]$$

QUESTION **58**

$$(35 + 37) \div 9 = [\,?\,] \div (4 \times 3)$$

KEEP GOING

In the following questions, three of the five words are related in some way.

Find the **two** words that do not go with these three and mark them **both** on the answer sheet.

Example

carrot   turnip   mango   pea   apple

Answer

mango   apple

QUESTION **59**

wet   moist   damp   tepid   cool

QUESTION **60**

sultana   current   fruit   raisin   prune

QUESTION **61**

trawler   vessel   barge   canoe   oar

QUESTION **62**

uncle   nephew   lass   farther   son

QUESTION **63**

oboe   flute   guitar   piano   clarinet

QUESTION **64**

peel   area   rind   acne   skin

QUESTION **65**

decrease   minimize   lesson   extend   shorten

QUESTION **66**

rarely   constantly   infrequently   seldom   often

GO STRAIGHT ON

Read the following information, then work out the correct answer to the question and mark it on the answer sheet.

QUESTION **67**

Four friends ordered pizza for supper.
Sahana, Natalie and Kapilan also ordered garlic bread.
Natalie and Claire ordered onion rings to go with their pizza.
Everyone, except Kapilan, drank Coke.

Which statement is true?

a. Kapilan is allergic to Coke.

b. Natalie doesn't like onions.

c. Sahana had everything

d. Claire did not order onion rings.

e. Natalie had everything.

GO STRAIGHT ON

ABCDEFGHIJKLMNOPQRSTUVWXYZ

The alphabet is here to help you with the following questions. Work out which pair of letters will come next in the series and mark your answer on the answer sheet.

Example

    LX   MW   NV   OU   [?]

Answer

          PT

QUESTION **68**

DV   GX   JZ   MB   PD   [?]

QUESTION **69**

HB   AB   JC   EC   LD   [?]

QUESTION **70**

CA   IB   ND   RG   UK   [?]

QUESTION **71**

FM   PW   GL   QV   HK   [?]

QUESTION **72**

MA   CB   OC   ED   QE   [?]

QUESTION **73**

OR   ST   WW   AA   EF   [?]

QUESTION **74**

AA   RS   DD   TU   GG   [?]

GO STRAIGHT ON

Three of these four words are written
in number code.

The codes are **not** written in the same order as the
words and one of the codes is missing.

MOOD   DEEM   DONE   MOON

2551   1332   1543

Work out the correct code for each word
and answer the following questions.

Mark the correct answer on the answer sheet.

QUESTION **75**

Which word has the number code **1543**?

QUESTION **76**

Find the code for the word **DOOM.**

.

QUESTION **77**

Find the code for the word **NEED.**

KEEP GOING

Three of these four words are written
in number code.

The codes are **not** written in the same order as the
words and one of the codes is missing.

DRAM   RARE   DARE   REAM

4215   6142   4142

Work out the correct code for each word
and answer the following questions.

Mark the correct answer on the answer sheet.

QUESTION **78**

Which word has the number code **64215**?

QUESTION **79**

Find the code for the word **DRAM.**

QUESTION **80**

Find the code for the word **DARE.**

END OF TEST 7

Paper 8

In the following questions, take a letter from the first word and move it into the second word to form two new words.

All the other letters must stay in the same order and both new words must make sense.

Work out which letter moves and mark it on the answer sheet.

Example

        heart   camp

Answer

    r   (the two new words
             are **heat** and **cramp**)

QUESTION **1**

blank   stale

QUESTION **2**

thump   peal

QUESTION **3**

moist   plan

QUESTION **4**

frame   towel

QUESTION **5**

table   cover

QUESTION **6**

chord   over

QUESTION **7**

cheat   spin

KEEP GOING

In these questions, find a letter that will complete the word in front of the brackets and begin the word after the brackets.
You must use the **same** letter in **both** sets of brackets.

Example

    tra   (?)   et
    man   (?)   es

Answer

    y (the four words are
          tray, yet, many, yes)

QUESTION **8**

wre   (?)   ail
ca   (?)   ear

QUESTION **9**

fel   (?)   oad
sa   (?)   all

QUESTION **10**

ran   (?)   ey
pac   (?)   ing

QUESTION **11**

tin   (?)   et
ba   (?)   es

QUESTION **12**

sta   (?)   ise
sti   (?)   um

QUESTION **13**

wil   (?)   evil
ho   (?)   are

QUESTION **14**

ach   (?)   ach
ar   (?)   ar

QUESTION **15**

ca   (?)   od
har   (?)   ail

GO STRAIGHT ON

A B C D E F G H I J K L M N O P Q R S T U V W X Y Z

The alphabet is here to help you with
the following questions.
Work out which pair of letters will
come next in the sequence and mark
your answer on the answer sheet.

Example

       AZ is to **BY**
       as
       CX is to [?]

Answer

                DW

QUESTION **16**

BT   is to   **YY**
as
LA   is to   [?]

QUESTION **17**

EO   is to   **AL**
as
BW   is to   [?]

QUESTION **18**

SB   is to   **PH**
as
OL   is to   [?]

QUESTION **19**

IJ   is to   **OE**
as
EQ   is to   [?]

QUESTION **20**

CW   is to   **ZZ**
as
WC   is to   [?]

KEEP GOING

QUESTION **21**

MA   is to   **TH**
as
BY   is to   [?]

QUESTION **22**

TV   is to   **XP**
as
YC   is to   [?]

Read the following information, then work
out the correct answer to the question and
mark its letter on the answer sheet.

QUESTION **23**

Kamal is 6 years old and Karim is 4.
In four years time Noah's age will equal the
combined ages of Kamal and Karim.

How old is Noah now?

a.   6

b.   8

c.   14

d.   12

e.   10

GO STRAIGHT ON

In each sentence there is a word of **four** letters hidden between the end of one word and the beginning of the next. Find the pair of words that contains the hidden word and mark your answer on the answer sheet.

Example

He skis so badly.

Answer

skis so (the hidden word is **kiss**)

QUESTION **24**

Play a tune on the piano.

QUESTION **25**

Peter left a little after six.

QUESTION **26**

Our old horse attempted a jump.

QUESTION **27**

Everyone was invited to the picnic.

QUESTION **28**

None of our family is lucky!

QUESTION **29**

Remember to sign at the bottom.

QUESTION **30**

They drink nothing but diet cola.

KEEP GOING

Read the information below and work out which statement is true.
Mark its letter on the answer sheet.

QUESTION **31**

On our last school trip, nobody was allowed to bring more than £20 pocket money.
Kyle brought twice as much money as George, but 10% less than Nilaani.
George had £5 more than Alex, who had £3 more than Tharani.
Nilaani brought the maximum amount.

a. Tharani brought the most money.

b. Kyle brought £19.

c. George brought £19.

d. Alex brought £4.

e. Tharani brought £3.

In each of the following questions, there is the same relationship between the word outside the brackets and a word inside each set of brackets. Choose **two** words, one from each set of brackets, that complete the sentence in the best way.

Example

cat is to
(tiger   kitten   calf)

as **dog** is to
(bone   kennel   puppy)

Answer

kitten   puppy

QUESTION **32**

cork is to
(bottle   lid   float)

as **lead** is to
(heavy   metal   sink)

GO STRAIGHT ON

QUESTION 33

car is to
(driver   petrol   vehicle)

as **house** is to
(window   garden   residence)

QUESTION 34

lenient is to
(slope   merciful   wobble)

as **brutal** is to
(harsh   animal   thrash)

QUESTION 35

pendulum is to
(beat   swing   hit)

as **propeller** is to
(turn   plane   strike)

QUESTION 36

auditary is to
(hear   touch   say)

as **visual** is to
(sense   see   smell)

QUESTION 37

stationary is to
(still   train   paper)

as **mobile** is to
(phone   moving   energetic)

QUESTION 38

winter is to
(beginning   cold   end)

as **spring** is to
(coil   start   leap)

GO STRAIGHT ON

A B C D E F G H I J K L M N O P Q R S T U V W X Y Z

The alphabet is here to help you with the following questions.
There is a different code for each question.
Find the correct answer and mark it on the answer sheet.

Example

If the code for **HARD** is **IBSE**,
what does **UFTU** mean?

Answer

TEST

QUESTION 39

If the code for **WRITE** is **AUKWI**,
what is the code for **PAPER**?

QUESTION 40

If the code for **CAFE** is **XZUV**,
what does **TIZY** mean?

QUESTION 41

If the code for **GLASS** is **NRFWV**,
what is the code for **METAL**?

QUESTION 42

If the code for **EAGLE** is **HYJJH**,
what does **IGQAK** mean?

QUESTION 43

If the code for **OPEN** is **TTHP**,
what is the code for **EXIT**?

QUESTION 44

If the code for **SWING** is **PADRD**,
what does **PPDHB** mean?

QUESTION 45

If the code for **PURSE** is **NRNPC**,
what is the code for **MONEY**?

GO STRAIGHT ON

In the following questions, find **two** words, one from each row, that are **most opposite in meaning.**

Example

(borrow   buy   sell)
(purchase   own   lend)

Answer
      borrow   lend

QUESTION **46**

(income   check   purchase)
(arrive   expenditure   cash)

QUESTION **47**

(indolent   industrious   idle)
(lazy   insolent   cheeky)

QUESTION **48**

(vital   essence   liquid)
(water   fluid   unessential)

QUESTION **49**

(fine   pay   reward)
(blame   penalize   lose)

QUESTION **50**

(abundant   keen   neat)
(scarce   plentiful   tidy)

QUESTION **51**

(water   field   barren)
(fertile   dessert   paddock)

QUESTION **52**

(victory   battle   loose)
(defeat   fight   win)

KEEP GOING

In the following series, find the number which comes next in the most sensible way, and mark it on your answer sheet.

Example

1   3   5   7   [?]

Answer
        9

QUESTION **53**

104   26   24   6   4   [?]

QUESTION **54**

1   3   6   10   15   [?]

QUESTION **55**

44   40   35   29   22   [?]

QUESTION **56**

3   6   8   16   18   [?]

QUESTION **57**

4   8   16   20   28   [?]

QUESTION **58**

3   9   6   18   15   [?]

QUESTION **59**

1   4   9   16   25   [?]

GO STRAIGHT ON

In each question there are two pairs of words. Only **one** of the answers will go equally well with **both** pairs of words.

Mark one word on the answer sheet.

Example

(just   reasonable)
(blonde   light)

Answer

fair

QUESTION **60**

(teach   train)
(bus   transport)

QUESTION **61**

(remainder   rest)
(stabilize   steady)

QUESTION **62**

(agreement   treaty)
(tighten   constrict)

QUESTION **63**

(mascot   talisman)
(beguile   entrance)

QUESTION **64**

(freezing   icy)
(sour   resentful)

QUESTION **65**

(light   faded)
(collapse   light-headed)

QUESTION **66**

(tax   levy)
(responsibility commitment)

KEEP GOING

In the following questions, the three numbers in **each** group are related in the **same** way.

Find the number which belongs with the last group and mark it on the answer sheet.

Example

(2 [6] 3)   (4 [8] 2)   (5 [?] 3)

Answer

15

QUESTION **67**

(8 [2] 12)   (6 [5] 16)   (12 [?] 24)

QUESTION **68**

(16 [10] 11)   (19 [8] 15)   (23 [?] 8)

QUESTION **69**

(11 [13] 5)   (9 [7] 6)   (13 [?] 7)

QUESTION **70**

(16 [26] 5)   (14 [32] 9)   (11 [?] 8)

QUESTION **71**

(6 [16] 4)   (10 [27] 7)   (11 [?] 5)

QUESTION **72**

(12 [48] 5)   (6 [12] 3)   (14 [?] 2)

QUESTION **73**

(49 [9] 7)   (56 [10] 7)   (32 [?] 8)

GO STRAIGHT ON

The word in brackets in the top row has been formed using the letters from the two words on either side.
Find the missing word in the second row that has been formed in the **same way** and mark your answer on the sheet.

Example

acre (actor) tore
care (?) melt

Answer

camel

QUESTION **74**

blue (pale) happy
calm (?) meter

QUESTION **75**

swim (trim) carrot
able (?) stamps

QUESTION **76**

match (cot) hot
freed (?) owe

QUESTION **77**

piano (page) gates
sweet (?) apple

QUESTION **78**

pencil (clean) water
sender (?) sweat

KEEP GOING

QUESTION **79**

fired (rage) grate
liner (?) meant

QUESTION **80**

pint (pain) neat
snow (?) gain

END OF TEST 8

ANSWERS

PAPER 5

1.	cot ton	59.	TEA
2.	peas ant	60.	BUT
3.	he art	61.	ran
4.	plum age	62.	seal
5.	can did	63.	open
6.	disc over	64.	mats
7.	at tack	65.	mead
8.	t	66.	fibre
9.	g	67.	seat
10.	e	68.	OE
11.	b	69.	YM
12.	e	70.	YK
13.	n	71.	PR
14.	e	72.	NO
15.	A	73.	EJ
16.	A	74.	WF
17.	C	75.	MEAN
18.	B	76.	4631
19.	B	77.	3265
20.	A	78.	STOW
21.	B	79.	1342
22.	e	80.	2312
23.	car engine		
24.	dog really		
25.	admit children		
26.	do men		
27.	the next		
28.	who made		
29.	games start		
30.	not allowed		
31.	vacant, empty		
32.	mint, parsley		
33.	sanctuary, safety		
34.	lobster, crab		
35.	friendly, sociable		
36.	hoax, trick		
37.	granite, marble		
38.	rehearsed, practised		
39.	valiant, courageous		
40.	core, heart		
41.	din, noise		
42.	consequence, outcome		
43.	height, altitude		
44.	recount, relate		
45.	shy, bashful		
46.	4		
47.	6		
48.	2		
49.	9		
50.	30		
51.	3		
52.	14		
53.	b		
54.	OUR		
55.	OWL		
56.	ERA		
57.	EAR		
58.	PET		

PAPER 6

1.	l	59.	AHBU
2.	k	60.	permit
3.	m	61.	lock
4.	b	62.	stop
5.	r	63.	file
6.	t	64.	spruce
7.	p	65.	entrance
8.	t	66.	fork
9.	s	67.	15
10.	p	68.	26
11.	l	69.	13
12.	r	70.	30
13.	l	71.	12
14.	r	72.	30
15.	QK	73.	13
16.	LF	74.	8
17.	QW	75.	cramp
18.	EP	76.	bear
19.	BL	77.	pole
20.	KC	78.	male
21.	FU	79.	bark
22.	D	80.	lead
23.	superior, inferior		
24.	squander, hoard		
25.	replicate, originate		
26.	trivial, important		
27.	coarse, fine		
28.	transparent, opaque		
29.	poverty, wealth		
30.	loiter, hasten		
31.	16		
32.	4		
33.	3		
34.	16		
35.	0.25		
36.	28		
37.	3		
38.	trip ended		
39.	give in		
40.	he irritates		
41.	train took		
42.	on certain		
43.	was perfect		
44.	show lasts		
45.	b		
46.	death, terminus		
47.	wind, string		
48.	hand, needle		
49.	mine, well		
50.	skin, shell		
51.	laugh, cry		
52.	ice, hail		
53.	GIQZO		
54.	BEANS		
55.	SBMHN		
56.	TREAD		
57.	UNMUV		
58.	PEACH		

## PAPER 7	## PAPER 8

PAPER 7

1.	might win	59.	tepid, cool
2.	his little	60.	current, fruit
3.	after many	61.	vessel, oar
4.	was late	62.	lass, farther
5.	conjuror entertained	63.	guitar, piano
6.	They escaped	64.	area, acne
7.	garden tonight	65.	extend, lesson
8.	n	66.	constantly, often
9.	b	67.	e
10.	w	68.	SF
11.	t	69.	ID
12.	b	70.	WP
13.	f	71.	RU
14.	w	72.	GF
15.	B	73.	IL
16.	B	74.	VW
17.	D	75.	DONE
18.	D	76.	1552
19.	A	77.	4331
20.	D	78.	DREAM
21.	A	79.	6415
22.	e	80.	6142
23.	vision, foresight		
24.	infectious, contagious		
25.	friend, ally		
26.	capitulate, surrender		
27.	dirty, soiled		
28.	everlasting, eternal		
29.	tolerate, accept		
30.	MAT		
31.	NET		
32.	EWE		
33.	OUR		
34.	SIN		
35.	BIT		
36.	TEN		
37.	loot		
38.	lamb		
39.	wade		
40.	laps		
41.	clean		
42.	salt		
43.	stinted		
44.	feat her		
45.	don ate		
46.	torn ado		
47.	at tempt		
48.	page ant		
49.	prim ate		
50.	come dies		
51.	par ties		
52.	7		
53.	12		
54.	2		
55.	9		
56.	3		
57.	7		
58.	96		

PAPER 8

1.	b	59.	36
2.	t	60.	coach
3.	i	61.	balance
4.	r	62.	contract
5.	t	63.	charm
6.	h	64.	bitter
7.	e	65.	faint
8.	n	66.	duty
9.	t	67.	6
10.	k	68.	30
11.	y	69.	13
12.	r	70.	27
13.	d	71.	27
14.	e	72.	14
15.	p	73.	6
16.	OF	74.	team
17.	XT	75.	sale
18.	LR	76.	ewe
19.	KL	77.	seal
20.	TF	78.	drawn
21.	IF	79.	name
22.	CW	80.	sing
23.	c		
24.	tune on		
25.	little after		
26.	horse attempted		
27.	the picnic		
28.	of our		
29.	sign at		
30.	drink nothing		
31.	d		
32.	float, sink		
33.	vehicle, residence		
34.	merciful, harsh		
35.	swing, turn		
36.	hear, see		
37.	still, moving		
38.	end, start		
39.	TDRHV		
40.	GRAB		
41.	TKYEO		
42.	FINCH		
43.	JBLV		
44.	SLIDE		
45.	KLJBW		
46.	income, expenditure		
47.	industrious, lazy		
48.	vital, unessential		
49.	reward, penalize		
50.	abundant, scarce		
51.	barren, fertile		
52.	victory, defeat		
53.	1		
54.	21		
55.	14		
56.	36		
57.	32		
58.	45		